For Jazz
~ J.T.

LITTLE TIGER PRESS LTD,
an imprint of the Little Tiger Group
1 Coda Studios, 189 Munster Road, London SW6 6AW
www.littletiger.co.uk

First published in Great Britain 2003
This edition published 2008

All rights reserved · ISBN 978-1-84506-827-1

Printed in China · LTP/2900/2775/0319

2 3 4 5 6 7 8 9 10

Andrew Murray

The Very Sleepy Sloth

Jack Tickle

LITTLE TIGER
LONDON

Deep in the jungle,
early in the morning,
the sloth was fast asleep.

But the rest of
the animals were
wide awake.

The cheetah was on
the running machine,
working on his

SPEED.

The elephant was lifting heavy weights, working on her

STRENGTH.

The kangaroo was
on the trampoline,
working on her

SPRING.

The monkey was
on the high bars,
working on his

SWING.

While the sloth stayed
in his hammock,
working on his sleep.

"That sloth is so lazy,"
said Cheetah.

"All he does is lie there!"
agreed Elephant.

"Just dozing in his hammock,"
added Kangaroo.

"Hey, Sloth!" called Monkey.
"We're all working hard here.
Why don't you get up and
do something?"

Sloth slowly opened one eye. "Monkey," he said. "If you're so hard-working, you try lifting Elephant's weights."

"Easy!" said Monkey,
and he tried to lift
the weights.
Elephant giggled as . . .

So Elephant tried to
jump on the trampoline.
Kangaroo tutted as . . .

CRASH!

Elephant fell right through.
"Don't tut at me, Kangaroo!"
said Elephant grumpily.
"Can *you* run like Cheetah?"

So Kangaroo tried the running machine.
Cheetah chuckled as Kangaroo
landed on . . .

her bottom!

OOOOOOW!

"Cheetah!" said Kangaroo crossly. "If you're so clever, you swing like Monkey."

So Cheetah climbed
the high bars and
swung right into . . .

By now, everyone was very hot,
very tired and very, very cross.

"This is useless," they muttered.
"Who caused all this trouble?"

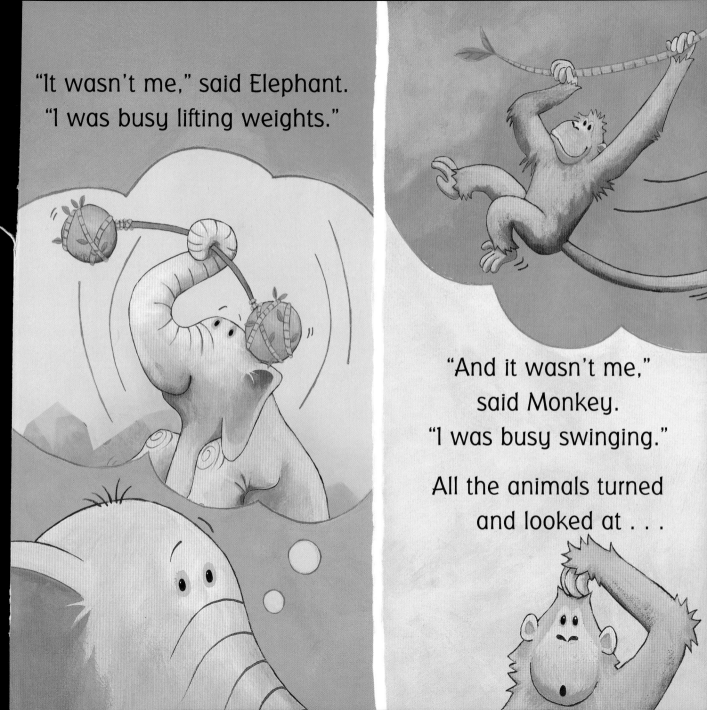

"It wasn't me," said Elephant.
"I was busy lifting weights."

"And it wasn't me,"
said Monkey.
"I was busy swinging."

All the animals turned
and looked at . . .

SLOTH!

"Hey, Sloth," they called.
"You started this!"

Sloth turned lazily.
"You must see by now,"
he said. "We were all busy doing
what we do best. Even me!"

The animals thought about it.
"Yes!" they cried. "We're all good at
running or jumping or lifting or swinging.
But Sloth is the very best at . . .

"SNO

OZING!"

"Exactly!" said Sloth.
And with a stretch
and a yawn he fell
fast asleep!

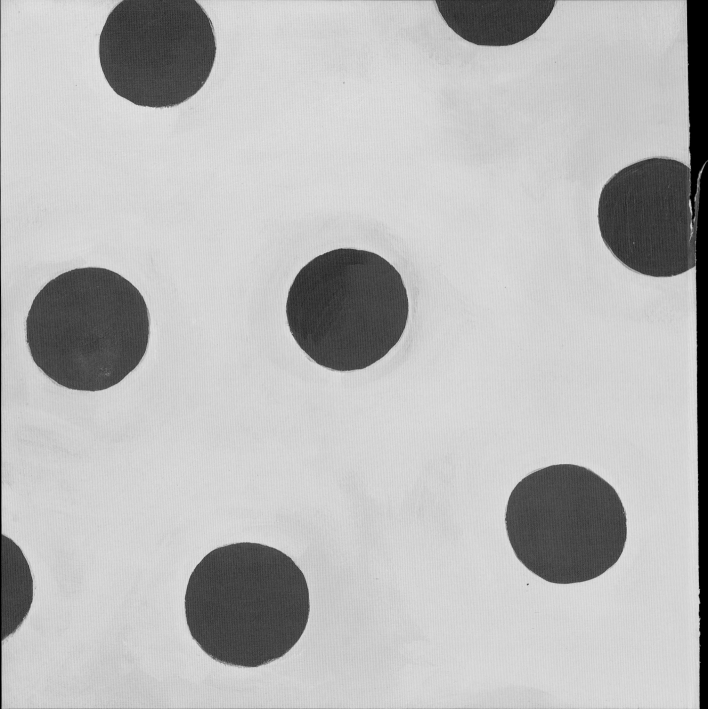

First Facts™

American Symbols

The Thomas Jefferson Memorial

by Terri DeGezelle

Consultant:
Melodie Andrews, Ph.D.
Associate Professor of Early American History
Minnesota State University, Mankato

Capstone press

Mankato, Minnesota

First Facts is published by Capstone Press
151 Good Counsel Drive, P.O. Box 669, Mankato, Minnesota 56002
www.capstonepress.com

Library of Congress Cataloging-in-Publication Data
DeGezelle, Terri 1955–
    The Thomas Jefferson Memorial / by Terri DeGezelle.
    p. cm.—(First Facts. American symbols)
    Summary: A simple introduction to the Thomas Jefferson Memorial, including its
history, designer, construction, location, and importance as a symbol of the United States.
    Includes bibliographical references and index.
    ISBN 0-7368-2531-2 (hardcover)
    1. Thomas Jefferson Memorial (Washington, D.C.)—Juvenile literature. 2. Jefferson,
Thomas, 1743–1826—Monuments—Washington (D.C.)—Juvenile literature. 3. Washington,
(D.C)—Buildings, structures, etc.—Juvenile literature. [1. Thomas Jefferson Memorial
(Washington, D.C.) 2. National monuments.] I. Title. II. Series: First Facts. American
symbols (Mankato, Minn.)
F203.4.J4D44 2004
973.4′6′092—dc21
                      2003011502

Editorial Credits
Roberta Schmidt, editor; Linda Clavel, series designer; Molly Nei, book designer and
    illustrator; Kelly Garvin and Scott Thoms, photo researchers; Eric Kudalis and Karen
    Risch, product planning editors

Photo Credits
Bruce Coleman Inc./J. Messerschmidt, 5, 19; Wendell Metzen, 16–17
Courtesy of Hagley Museum and Library, 11
Folio Inc./Cameron Davidson, cover (left); Fred J. Maroon, 9, 18
North Wind Picture Archives, 6–7, 15, 20
PhotoDisc Inc., cover (right), 13

1 2 3 4 5 6 09 08 07 06 05 04

Table of Contents

Thomas Jefferson Memorial Fast Facts

- The Thomas Jefferson Memorial honors Thomas Jefferson. He was the third president of the United States.

- American architect John Russell Pope designed the Thomas Jefferson Memorial. When Pope died in 1937, Daniel P. Higgins and Otto R. Eggers took over the project.

- The bronze statue is the second statue of Jefferson to stand in the memorial. The first statue was made of plaster. It was replaced after World War II (1939–1945), when metal once again became available.

- The cherry blossom trees near the Thomas Jefferson Memorial were a gift from Tokyo, Japan, to Washington, D.C.

Symbol of Independence and Freedom

The Thomas Jefferson **Memorial** is a **symbol** of **independence** and **freedom**. It reminds people of President Thomas Jefferson. Jefferson helped the American colonies win independence from Great Britain. He believed all people should be free.

 **Fun Fact:**
The Thomas Jefferson Memorial looks similar to Jefferson's home, Monticello, in Virginia.

7

Jefferson and the United States

Thomas Jefferson played an important part in U.S. history. Jefferson was the main writer of the **Declaration of Independence**. He was an important part of the U.S. government after the Revolutionary War (1775–1783). Jefferson was the third president.

 **Fun Fact:**

Thomas Jefferson loved vegetables. He grew many types of squash, broccoli, beans, and peas in his garden.

9

A Memorial Building

In 1934, Congress decided to make a building to remember Jefferson. Three years later, a place for the memorial was chosen in Washington, D.C.

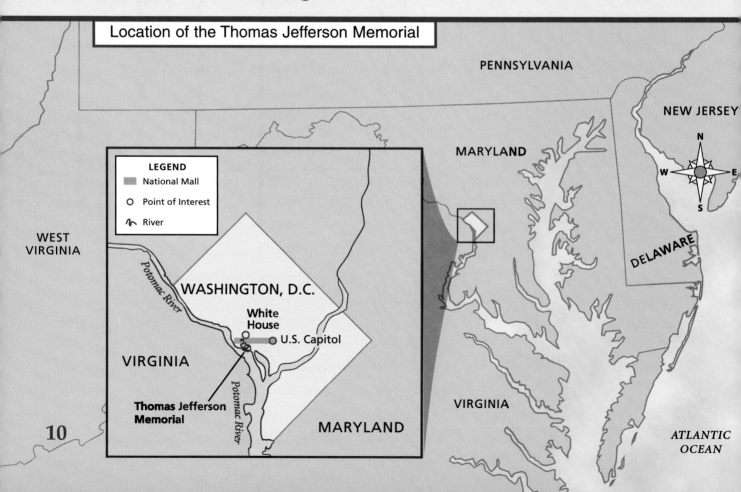

Location of the Thomas Jefferson Memorial

LEGEND
National Mall
○ Point of Interest
River

PENNSYLVANIA

NEW JERSEY

MARYLAND

WEST VIRGINIA

WASHINGTON, D.C.

White House

○ U.S. Capitol

VIRGINIA

Potomac River

Thomas Jefferson Memorial

MARYLAND

DELAWARE

VIRGINIA

ATLANTIC OCEAN

10

Work on the memorial began in 1938. Workers made the building out of a hard stone called marble. The Thomas Jefferson Memorial was finished in 1943.

The Statue of Thomas Jefferson

The large **statue** of Jefferson is an important part of the memorial. Rudolph Evans designed the statue. He showed how Jefferson looked when he spoke to Congress. The statue holds a copy of the Declaration of Independence in its left hand.

Fun Fact:
The statue of Jefferson is 19 feet (5.8 meters) tall. It weighs 5 tons (4.5 metric tons).

The Memorial Writings

Jefferson was a powerful speaker and writer. Some of his famous words are carved into the walls of the memorial building. One wall has words from the Declaration of Independence on it.

WE HOLD THESE TRUTHS TO BE SELF-
EVIDENT: THAT ALL MEN ARE CREATED
EQUAL, THAT THEY ARE ENDOWED BY THEIR
CREATOR WITH CERTAIN INALIENABLE
RIGHTS, AMONG THESE ARE LIFE, LIBERTY
AND THE PURSUIT OF HAPPINESS, THAT
TO SECURE THESE RIGHTS GOVERNMENTS
ARE INSTITUTED AMONG MEN. WE···
SOLEMNLY PUBLISH AND DECLARE, THAT
THESE COLONIES ARE AND OF RIGHT
OUGHT TO BE FREE AND INDEPENDENT
STATES···AND FOR THE SUPPORT OF THIS
DECLARATION, WITH A FIRM RELIANCE
ON THE PROTECTION OF DIVINE
PROVIDENCE, WE MUTUALLY PLEDGE
OUR LIVES, OUR FORTUNES AND OUR
SACRED HONOUR.

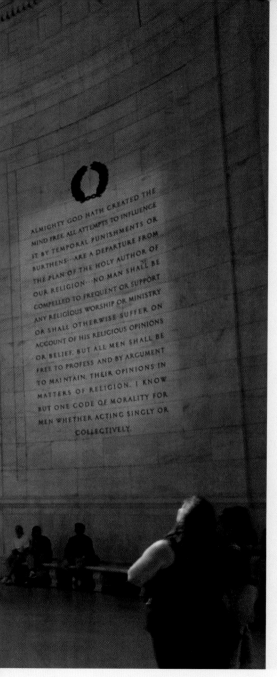

The Thomas Jefferson Memorial Today

The Thomas Jefferson Memorial is an important American symbol. Each year, millions of people visit the memorial. They remember Jefferson and his work for independence and freedom.

 **Fun Fact:**
Many people go to the memorial to celebrate Easter, Memorial Day, and the Cherry Blossom Festival.

Time Line

1743—Thomas Jefferson is born in Virginia.

1826—Jefferson dies.

1775–1776—Jefferson helps write the Declaration of Independence.

1801–1809—Jefferson serves as president of the United States.

1938—Work begins on the Thomas Jefferson Memorial.

1943—The Thomas Jefferson Memorial is dedicated on the 200th anniversary of Jefferson's birthday.

Amazing But True!

Above the memorial's entrance is a sculpture of the Declaration Committee. The men in the committee helped Jefferson write the Declaration of Independence. Jefferson is shown with John Adams, Benjamin Franklin, Robert Livingston, and Roger Sherman.

Hands On: Draw a Memorial

The Thomas Jefferson Memorial was designed to remind people of Jefferson and the things he believed in. What would a memorial for you look like?

What You Need

paper
crayons

What You Do

1. Think of how you want your building to look. Jefferson's memorial looks like his house.
2. Draw a picture of your building.
3. The walls of Jefferson's memorial have cornstalks, scrolls, and columns on them. These objects represent Jefferson's interest in agriculture, writing and education, and architecture. Think of objects that stand for you and what you like to do. Do you like books, animals, or toys? Draw these objects on the walls of your memorial.
4. Draw a statue of yourself in the memorial. Is the statue standing or sitting? Does the statue have anything in its hands?

Glossary

Declaration of Independence (dek-luh-RAY-shuhn UHV in-di-PEN-duhnss)—a paper declaring the freedom of the 13 American colonies from the rule of Great Britain

freedom (FREE-duhm)—the right to live the way you want

independence (in-di-PEN-duhnss)—freedom from the control of other people or things

memorial (muh-MOR-ee-uhl)—something that is built or done to help people remember a person or event

statue (STACH-oo)—something carved or shaped out of stone, wood, or other material

symbol (SIM-buhl)—an object that stands for something else

Read More

Ferry, Joseph. *The Jefferson Memorial.* American Symbols and Their Meanings. Philadelphia: Mason Crest, 2003.

Stone, Tanya Lee. *America's Top 10 National Monuments.* America's Top 10. Woodbridge, Conn.: Blackbirch Press, 1998.

Internet Sites

FactHound offers a safe, fun way to find Internet sites related to this book. All of the sites on FactHound have been researched by our staff.

Here's how:
1. Visit *www.facthound.com*
2. Type in this special code **0736825312** for age-appropriate sites. Or enter a search word related to this book for a more general search.
3. Click on the **Fetch It** button.

FactHound will fetch the best sites for you!

Index